Sports Day

Written by **Nicola Fairbairn**

Illustrated by **Ruth Hearson**

It was a sunny day
in the middle of July.

Everyone was sitting at the table eating breakfast.

Joshua was very excited because today was their school sports day.

"I am going to win so many medals!" he said, rocking his chair from side to side.

"You hope you will," said Daddy.

"Please sit still," said Mummy.

"I'm the fastest runner in my class,"

said Joshua smiling proudly.

"I'm rubbish at running," said Rosie looking fed up.

"That's not true," said Daddy.

"Yes it is. I wish I didn't have to go to school today."

"Well I can't wait!" exclaimed Joshua,

"I really really hope I do get a medal."

Rosie looked even more fed up.

"Ok you two," Mummy began, "Let's stop talking about sports day for a minute."

She went to the shelf and found her Bible. "I want you to listen to what God tells us he is like. In this part of the Bible he is helping Samuel to choose a new king."

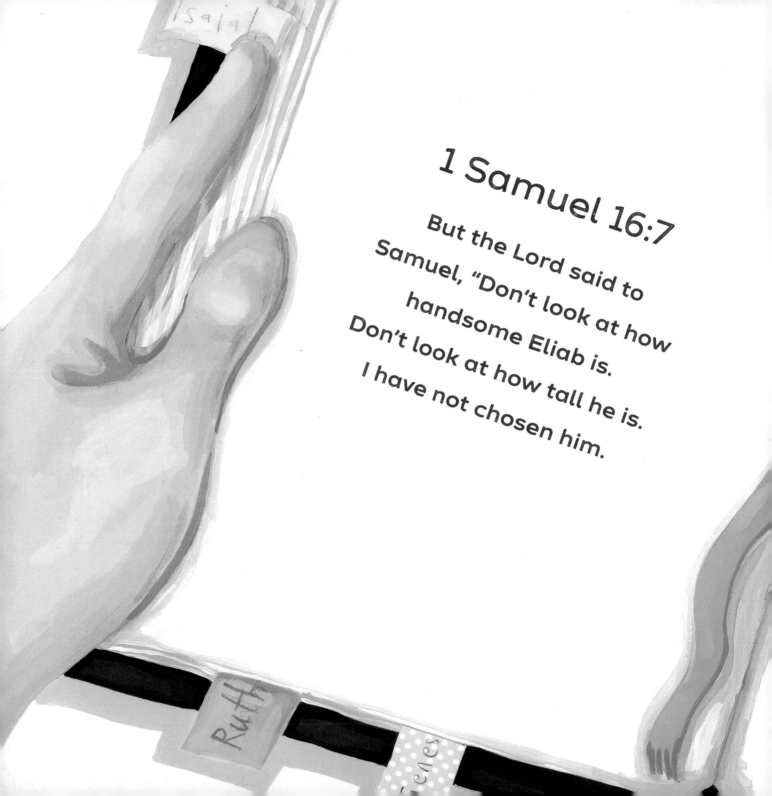

1 Samuel 16:7

But the Lord said to Samuel, "Don't look at how handsome Eliab is. Don't look at how tall he is. I have not chosen him.

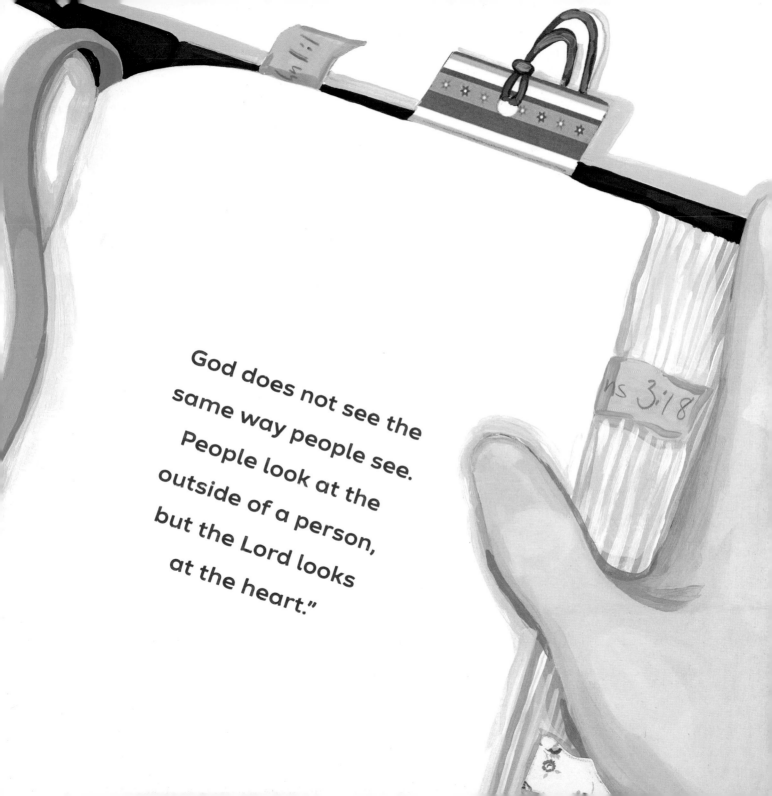

God does not see the
same way people see.
People look at the
outside of a person,
but the Lord looks
at the heart."

"You see, sometimes we think what matters most is how many things we are good at but God says the most important thing to him is what we're like on the inside."

"We can pray that you both try your best today and most importantly use your hearts to love God and other people."

So Mummy prayed for the children and then they went upstairs to get ready for the day.

At the end of the afternoon, Mummy
was sitting down feeding Abigail.

Suddenly the door burst open and Joshua, Rosie
and Daddy came in buzzing with excitement.

They began to tell Mummy all about sports day.

Joshua had won second

place in the relay race.

Rosie had managed to do the egg and
spoon race without dropping the egg!

And Daddy had won first prize in the Fathers' Race.

"I even got a medal!"
Daddy said proudly.

"Yes, but remember Dad, God is more interested in your heart!"

"Oh yes Josh, you're absolutely right!"
he replied, and they all laughed.

For all the children and grown ups
at Bumpkins Toddler group – NF

For the wonderful Purkiss family – RH

Sports Day

Text © 2019 Nicola Fairbairn
Illustrations © 2019 Ruth Hearson

Scriptures quoted from the International Children's Bible®, copyright ©1986, 1988, 1999, 2015 by Tommy Nelson. Used by permission.

Published by 10Publishing, a division of 10ofThose Limited.

ISBN: 978-1-912373-73-4

Typeset by Diane Warnes
Printed in China

10Publishing, a division of 10ofthose.com
Unit C, Tomlinson Road, Leyland, Lancashire, PR25 2DY England
Email: info@10ofthose.com
Website: www.10ofthose.com

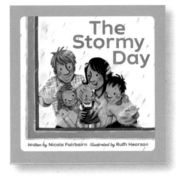

10Publishing is committed to publishing
quality Christian resources that are biblical,
accessible and point people to Jesus.

www.10ofthose.com is our online retail partner
selling thousands of quality books at discounted prices.

For information contact: info@10ofthose.com
or check out our website: www.10ofthose.com